Letts

Framework FOCUS

EXERCISE BANK · EXERCISE BANK · EXERCISE BANK · EXERCISE BANK ·

Using and Applying Mathematics to Solve Problems

Steve Mills and Hilary Koll

Published by Letts Educational
The Chiswick Centre
414 Chiswick High Road
London W4 5TF
tel: 020 89963333
fax: 020 87428390
email: mail@lettsed.co.uk
website: www.letts-education.com

Letts Educational is part of the Granada Learning Group. Granada Learning is a division of Granada plc.

First published 2003

ISBN 1 84085 8877

British Library Cataloguing in Publication Data

A catalogue record for this book is available from the British Library.

Commissioned by Helen Clark

Project management by Vicky Butt

Cover design by bigtop, Bicester, UK

Editorial, layout and illustration by Hart McLeod, Cambridge

Production by PDQ

Printed and bound by Canale, Italy

Contents

YEAR 7

YEAR 8

Objectives are numbered consecutively within each topic as laid out in the Mathematics Framework, pages 6–11. Objectives listed in bold type are Key Objectives.
U = Using and applying mathematics to solve problems
C = Calculations

YEAR 9

	Framework objective	Page
Solving word problems	*U1*	40
Identifying information	U2	45
Breaking into steps	U3, C6, C7	47
Establishing solutions 1	*U4*, C8	51
Establishing solutions 2	*U4*, C8,	56
Investigating and generalising	*U5*	60

Objectives are numbered consecutively within each topic as laid out in the Mathematics Framework, pages 6–11. Objectives listed in bold type are Key Objectives. Objectives in italic are listed in the Framework as containing material suitable for more able students.
U = Using and applying mathematics to solve problems
C = Calculations

How to use this book

The Letts *Exercise Bank* series has been written specifically to match the Framework for Teaching Mathematics. Each book contains exercises focused on a particular Framework topic, and can be used alongside any course or Scheme of Work.

The book is clearly divided into work for Years 7, 8 and 9. Each unit contains Essential Exercises, Consolidation Exercises and Challenging Exercises.

Throughout this book you will see the following symbols:

✓ This indicates a 'self test' question. Pupils can check their understanding of each unit by using the answers provided at the back of the book (page 64).

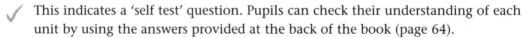 This indicates that a calculator is required.

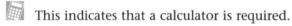 Questions featuring this symbol are intended as homework.

SOLVING WORD PROBLEMS 7

MONEY AND PERCENTAGES

Essential Exercises

1 A T-shirt and a cap together cost £9. Two T-shirts and a cap cost £14.50. How much does one cap cost?

2 One can of cola and a chocolate bar cost 80p. Three cans of cola and a chocolate bar cost £1.70. What does the chocolate bar cost?

3 Sam paid 30% of the price of a new £12 000 Nexus 1.6 Hatchback in cash. How much cash did she pay?

Consolidation Exercises

4 One CD and a cassette tape cost £19. Four CDs and a cassette tape cost £58. What is the cost of one CD?

5 Which is greater: 25% of £5 or 75% of £1.60?

6 Which is less: 40% of £12 or 90% of £5?

7 The value of a £70 000 house increased by 14% in May and by a further 9% in July. What was its new value?

Challenging Exercises

8 In April, the cost of a new £125 graphite tennis racket increased by 8%. Before the end of the season the price was reduced by 15%. What was the end of season price?

9 ✓ A cup of tea and three cakes cost £3. Two cups of tea and two cakes cost £3.60. Three cups and one cake cost £4.20. How much does one cake cost?

10 Draw up a table to show the cost of any combination of up to four teas and cakes in **9**. You might record it in a table like this.

Number of teas	Number of cakes			
	1	2	3	4
1			£3	
2		£3.60		
3	£4.20			
4				

7 SOLVING WORD PROBLEMS

NUMBER AND ALGEBRA

Essential Exercises

1 Complete this multiplication square.

×	5		8	
	20		32	
			72	
2		14		6
	30			

2 A number sequence is made from cubes.

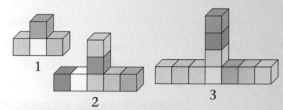

How many cubes will be in the:

a sixth shape   **b** tenth shape?

3 By putting different numbers in the square, triangle and circle find five ways of completing each of these equations.

a $\square + \triangle + \bigcirc = 1$

b $\square - \triangle - \bigcirc = 0.1$

Consolidation Exercises

4 I'm thinking of a number. If I add 4.2 and multiply by 3 the answer is 21.9. What is my number?

5 The sum of two square numbers is 65. What are they?

6 What is the perimeter and area of a square where each side is $3a$ long?

Challenging Exercises

7 When two prime numbers are added the total is 52. How many different pairs of primes could this be? What are they?

8 ✓ A machine changes the value of a number from n to $2n - 1$.

What will the value of these numbers change to?

a 6   **b** 9   **c** 15   **d** 7.5

SOLVING WORD PROBLEMS 7

RATIO AND PROPORTION

Essential Exercises

1 A packet of Whizzoes has 3 red sweets in every 8 sweets. There are 32 sweets in a packet. How many are red sweets

2 A girl bought a top and a skirt, costing £36 in total. She spent three times as much on the skirt as on the top. How much was the skirt?

3 There are 288 books in the bookshop. 216 of these are novels and the rest are non-fiction. 36 of the books in the shop are in the sale.

  a How many books are non-fiction?

  b What proportion of the books are in the sale?

Consolidation Exercises

4 A shop has a 'buy 3 get 1 free' offer on make-up. Jo leaves the shop with 16 items and Emma leaves with 24. How many items did each girl buy?

5 This table shows the attendance for evening classes at the local college.

  a Write the male/female ratio for each class in its simplest form.

  b Write the number of males and females as a proportion of the total attendance for each course.

Subject	Number of males	females
Geology	6	9
Greek (beginners)	12	8
Art	8	16
Yoga	10	25

Challenging Exercises

6 A recipe for vegetable soup needs 5 carrots for every $1\frac{1}{2}$ litres of soup.

  a How many carrots are needed to make 9 litres of soup?

  b How much soup can be made if you have 25 carrots?

7 1 euro = £0.60. How much is: **a** 8 euros in pounds **b** £3 in euros

8 ✓ Doug makes 75 litres of compost. How many litres does he use:

  a of soil   **b** of peat   **c** of sand?

Compost mix
7 parts soil
5 parts peat
3 parts sand

SOLVING WORD PROBLEMS

SHAPE AND SPACE

Essential Exercises

1 Here are three shapes made from four squares which join along the length of one or more edges.

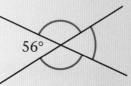

  a Draw two more.

  b Which of the shapes have line symmetry?

2 a Find the missing angles in this diagram.

  b Explain how you worked them out.

56°

3 In how many ways can the inside of a matchbox fit into its cover? Think carefully. It's more than two! Record each way in your book.

Challenging Exercises

4 You can split a square into 3 regions using 2 lines, like this …

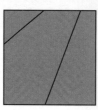

or you can use 2 lines to split the square into 4 regions, like this.

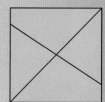

What is the smallest number of lines needed to create:

  a 6 regions

  b 9 regions?

Draw your answers.

5 Draw a table to show the maximum number of regions that can be made using up to 6 lines.

Number of lines	0	1	2	3	4	5	6
Maximum number of regions							

6 🏠 Investigate the minimum numbers of lines needed to make different numbers of regions in a circle.

SOLVING WORD PROBLEMS

MEASURES

Essential Exercises

1 Here are three shapes made from five squares which join along the length of one or more edges.

You can make 12 different shapes from five squares.

a Using 1 cm squares, draw as many shapes from five squares as you can.

b Next to each shape write its area and perimeter.

Consolidation Exercises

2 This is an aerial view of part of a tiled floor.

The two yellow squares cover $\frac{1}{3}$ of the total area.

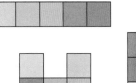
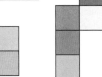
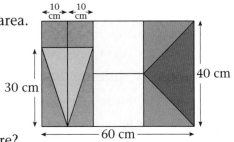

a What is the area of:

   i one green right-angled triangle

   ii the space coloured pink

   iii the red triangle?

b What is the perimeter of one yellow square?

c The perimeter of one blue triangle is 68.3 cm. What is the length of its longest side?

Challenging Exercises

3 ✓ 🖩 A kilogram box of tomatoes costs £1.50. Each tomato weighs 120 g. What is the cost of one tomato?

4 Each day Ben leaves school at 15:50 and arrives home at 16:35, except on Mondays when the journey is 5 minutes quicker.

How long does Ben spend travelling home over:

a one week **b** a 14-week term

c a 39-week year?

5 🏠 Investigate how long you spend travelling home over the same periods as in question **4**.

7 SOLVING WORD PROBLEMS

HANDLING DATA AND PROBABILITY

Essential Exercises

1 Dev has made a six-sided spinner. What is the probability of it landing on:

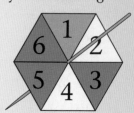

- **a** blue
- **b** red
- **c** yellow
- **d** an even number
- **e** 5
- **f** ✓ a multiple of 2?

2 Find three different numbers which have a mean of 7.

Consolidation Exercises

3 Wayne has recorded the number of letters in the first names of the pupils in his class and has drawn a bar chart to show this information.

He says 'Most first names have fewer than six letters.'

Explain why he might be wrong.

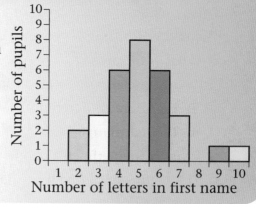

Challenging Exercises

4 Write five numbers with a:

- **a** mean of 6
- **b** mode of 5
- **c** median of 5.

5 Design an eight-sided spinner using the numbers 7–14.

Write probability questions about it to match these answers:

- **a** $\frac{1}{8}$
- **b** $\frac{1}{4}$
- **c** $\frac{3}{8}$
- **d** $\frac{3}{4}$

IDENTIFYING INFORMATION

Essential Exercises

1 a Draw a triangle in your book, using a pencil and ruler. Hide it and describe it to a partner.

Think about:

   i the lengths of the sides

   ii the size of the angles

   iii whether any sides are vertical or horizontal.

b Ask your partner to draw the triangle from your description.

c Did you give enough information?

d Was other information necessary? If so, what was it?

Swap roles and try again.

2 Dodgy calculators!

The number 6 button on your calculator doesn't work.

Find and record three ways to display each of the following numbers.

  a 66   **b** 606   **c** 968   **d** 1006   **e** 2626   **f** 6666

For example [5] [8] [+] [8] [=] 66

You can use all the other keys, including +, −, ×, ÷ and = .

Consolidation Exercises

3 a Draw three letters on a piece of paper.

They can be different sizes and even reversed.

b Without letting your partner see your sheet describe what you have drawn.

Think about the size, position and orientation of the letters.

c Ask your partner to draw an identical copy.

d Swap roles and try again.

e Write a report on the activity. Include things like the information you gave, whether it was enough and whether other information was needed.

4 Suppose none of the even numbers on your calculator works!

Find three ways to display each of the following:

a 24   **b** 312   **c** 836   **d** 1010   **e** 1436   **f** 2468

For example 3 1 − 7 = 24

Record your methods.

Challenging Exercises

5 a Draw some symbols or shapes on a piece of paper. Without letting your partner see your drawing describe what you have drawn. Your partner has to draw an identical copy based on your information. Think carefully about what information you have to give. Swap roles and try this several times.

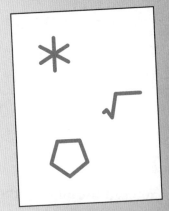

b Write a report on the activity.

6 Suppose these are the only keys on your calculator that work.

 3 4 8 9 + − × ÷ = ( )

Find as many ways as you can to display each of the following:

a 6   **b** 33   **c** 41   **d** 68   **e** 60   **f** 70

For example 3 + 3 = 6

Don't forget to record each of your solutions.

7 🏠 Using the same keys as in question **6**, how many numbers between 50 and 60 can you make?

BREAKING INTO STEPS

Essential Exercises

1 Answer these questions.

   a How many minutes in one hour?   **b** How many seconds in one minute?

   c How many weeks in one year?   **d** How many days in one week?

   e How many hours in one day?   **f** How many months in one year?

   g How many days in one year (not a leap year)?

2 Break this problem into smaller steps to help you solve it.

Over a year, a famous footballer earns on average £1200 per day.

His wife, a super-model, earns on average 88p per minute for every minute of the day.

   a Who earns more?   **b** How much do they each earn in a year?

3 Copy and complete this diagram.

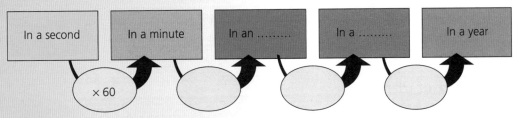

4 Try this.

Ali:
> Over a year I earn, on average, £6 per hour.

Ben:
> Over a year I earn, on average, £800 per week.

Chloe:
> Over a year I earn, on average, 2p per second.

   a Who earns the most in a year?

   b How much do they each earn in a year?

5 The local grocer's shop has a pair of balance scales and the following weights:

one 10 kg, one 6 kg, one 2 kg and one 1 kg.

Show how the grocer can weigh 5 kg of potatoes using these weights.

6 Look at the design on the right. It is made from triangles.

a Estimate how many triangles there are.

Think about:

i the different sizes of triangles, e.g.

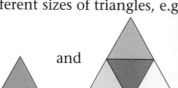

and

ii their different orientations, e.g.

 and

b Can you find the exact number of triangles?

Think about how you will record your findings, e.g.

Size of triangle			
Number	?	?	?

Consolidation Exercises

7 ✓ Explain how the grocer in question **5** could weigh accurately 14 kg of potatoes.

8 This grocer has lots of weights, but they're all either 10 kg weights or 7 kg weights. Make a table to show how many kilograms, up to 30 kg, she could weigh accurately using as many 10 kg and 7 kg weights as she needs.

You could record it like this:

To weigh	Weights	
	Left-hand 10 kg	Right-hand 7 kg
1 kg	2	3
2 kg		
3 kg		

9 Continue the table in question **8** up to 50 kg.

10 Using a similar approach, solve these problems.

A famous pop star earns £768 000 in one year.

Write the average amount earned each:

a day **b** minute **c** week

d hour **e** month **f** second.

g Write in words how you worked out each answer above.

h A quick way of calculating the average amount per second is to divide the year's earnings by a number. What is this number?

11 **a** Using what you have learnt from question **6**, can you now find the number of triangles in this design?

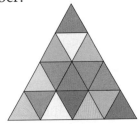

b Do you think this design will have more or fewer triangles than the design in **b**?

Count the number of triangles to find out. How many are there?

Think carefully about how you will make sure you have counted them all.

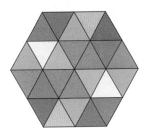

Challenging Exercises

12 Use what you have learnt from the other exercises to help you answer this question.

A director of a company earns £1 825 000 in one year.

Approximately how many days does it take her to earn one million pounds?

13 Write a formula, for a computer, that will convert a month's pay into an average amount per second.

14 How many years old are you?

Work out approximately how many days, hours, minutes and seconds old you are.

Be as accurate as you can. Include leap years.

15 a How many squares are in this design?

b Write a report, describing how you tackled the activity, what you found and how you recorded your results.

c How could you use your results to predict the number of squares in a 6 × 6 square?

d Can you find a rule for the number of the smallest squares in an $n \times n$ square?

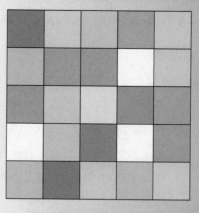

16 How many cubes are in this shape?

Remember to include different sized cubes.

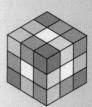

Essential Exercises

1 Create new numbers in the chains by adding the two preceding numbers, like this: 3 + 5 = 8

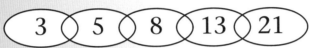

(3)(5)(8)(13)(21)

Try these in the same way.

a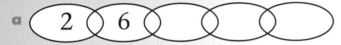

(2)(6)( )( )( )

b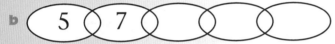

(5)(7)( )( )( )

c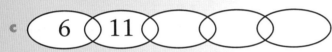

(6)(11)( )( )( )

2 Write down any three consecutive numbers, for example 6, 7 and 8.

Find the product of the highest and lowest numbers   6 × 8 = 48

Square the middle number   7 × 7 = 49

a Try this for six sets of three consecutive numbers.

b What do you notice?

c What do you notice if you use three consecutive even numbers?

6   7   8

Consolidation Exercises

3 ✓ Try these using the same rule as in question **1**.

a

(4)( )(9)( )( )

b

(2)( )( )(14)( )

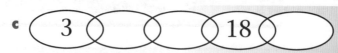

c (3)( )( )(18)( )

d Draw two chains of your own that have 20 as the fourth number.

4 Try the activity in question **2** using three consecutive decimal numbers, like 5.1, 5.2 and 5.3.

5.1 5.2 5.3

a Try this for six sets of three consecutive numbers.

b What do you notice?

c What happens if you use decimals to 2 places, like 4.23, 4.24 and 4.25?

d What if you use three numbers like 2.4, 2.6 and 2.8?

Challenging Exercises

5 Try these.

a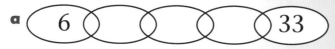

(6)( )( )( )(33)

b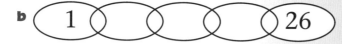

(1)( )( )( )(26)

c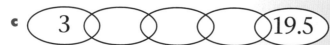

(3)( )( )( )(19.5)

d Explain the method you used to complete each chain in **a**, **b** and **c**.

e Draw as many chains as you can that have 26 as the last number.

6

Problems on the river!

Two women and two girls are out walking. They reach a deep river they want to cross.

There is a boat but it can hold only:

- one woman or
- one girl or
- two girls.

It cannot hold the two women together.

a Explain how they can all cross the river.

b Think carefully how you would record their movements.

7 Choose a number between 30 and 40 and draw as many chains as you can with that as the last number.

INVESTIGATING AND GENERALISING

Essential Exercises

1 Can you find a number with exactly three factors? What about a number with exactly four factors?

a Complete this table for the numbers between 15 and 30.

Number	Factors	Number of factors
15	1, 3, 5, 15	4
16		

b List the numbers with an odd number of factors.

c What do you notice about these numbers?

d Test your idea by trying other similar numbers.

2 ✓ Look at this sequence of counters.

a How many counters are there in:

   i term 1   **ii** term 2

   iii term 3?

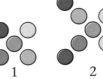 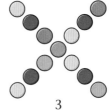

Term   1   2   3

b Can you see a pattern in your numbers? Explain your pattern in words.

c Can you predict the number of counters in:

   i the fifth term   **ii** the eighth term?

3 Zip Zap!

This 3 × 3 grid is made by using the digits from 1 to 9 once only. It shows six 3-digit numbers.

'Zap' numbers, like 351, go across and 'Zip' numbers, like 392, go down.

Describe each number using words like prime, multiple, factor, square, product, even, odd, greater than, less than, between, consecutive, sum, total, difference, etc.

	Zip 1 ↓	Zip 2 ↓	Zip 3 ↓
Zap 1 →	3	5	1
Zap 2 →	9	8	7
Zap 3 →	2	4	6

Zap 1 is a multiple of 9 between 300 and 400.

Zap 2 ....

Zap 3 ....

Zip 1 ....

Zip 2 ....

Zip 3 ....

4 Solve this Zip Zap puzzle.

Across

Zap 1 is an odd number between 700 and 800.

Zap 2 is less than 300. Its digits are three consecutive multiples of 2.

Zap 3 is a multiple of 19. It is an odd number.

Down

Zip 1 is a multiple of 25. Its first digit equals the sum of the second two digits.

Zip 2 is even and between 130 and 160.

Zip 3 is made from three consecutive multiples of 3.

Zip 1 ↓	Zip 2 ↓	Zip 3 ↓
Zap 1 →	1	
Zap 2 →	4	
Zap 3 →	8	

Consolidation Exercises

5 This diagram shows an addition pyramid with a top number of 44.

Each number is the sum of the two numbers beneath it.

	44		
	20	24	
	9	11	13
7	2	9	4

a Use the numbers 2, 4, 7 and 9 as base numbers. Arrange them to create:

   i the largest possible top number

  ii the smallest possible top number.

b Explain how, with a different set of base numbers, you could quickly work out which arrangements would give the largest and smallest top numbers.

6 Function machines change input numbers to create new output numbers. They change each number in the same way.

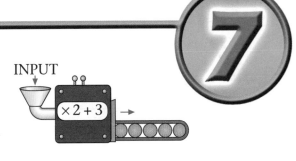

This function machine has the rule × 2 + 3.

a ✓ Input the numbers 3, 4 and 5. What are the output numbers?

b Here is another machine with its input and output numbers shown. Find its rule and give some examples of other input and output numbers that match the rule.

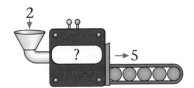

INPUT		OUTPUT
2	→	5
6	→	17
4	→	11
3	→	8

7 a 🏠 242 is a palindromic number because the digits are the same when reversed. How many palindromic numbers are there between:

   i 10 and 100   **ii** 100 and 1000?

b Using the information from **ai** and **aii**, can you predict how many there will be between:

   i 1000 and 10 000   **ii** 10 000 and 100 000   **iii** 10 and 1 000 000?

   Test your predictions.

8 Solve this Zip Zap puzzle. Forgotten the rules? See question **3** on page 19.

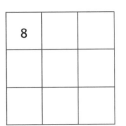

Across

Zap 1 is a square number less than 1000.
Zap 2 has the prime factors 3, 5 and 7.
Zap 3 is a prime number between 260 and 270.

Down

Zip 1 is an even number, exactly divisible by 8 and 109.
Zip 2 is exactly half of Zip 1.
Zip 3 the sum of its digits is 15 and it is a multiple of 3.

9

| 1 cm | 2 cm | | 5 cm | 7 cm | | 10 cm |

This ruler, even though it only has five measurements marked, allows you to measure all whole centimetre lengths between 1 and 10 centimetres. For example, you can measure 4 cm like this:

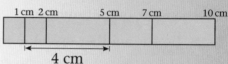

4 cm

Design a different ruler with five markings that allows you to measure all whole centimetre lengths between 1 and 10 centimetres.

10 This grid uses each of the digits 1 to 9 once only. The totals of the rows, columns and diagonals in the grid are shown. Some totals are odd, some are even.

3	5	2	→10
1	6	7	→14
8	4	9	→21

↙ 16   ↓ 12   ↓ 15   ↓ 18   ↘ 18

a Using the digits 1 to 9 once only, can you make the totals of each of the rows, columns and diagonals in the grid odd numbers?

b How many different ways can you find?

c Describe one of your ways in a grid using the letters E (for an even number) and O (for an odd number).

11

> A prime number has exactly two factors, itself and 1. So 5, 17 and 23 are primes.

> You get a square number when you multiply a whole number by itself. 25 is square because 5×5 equals 25.

a Write out the first 12 square numbers.

b Here is a list of primes between 70 and 200.

| 71 | 73 | 79 | 83 | 97 | 101 | 103 | 107 | 109 | 113 | 127 | 131 | 137 |
| 139 | 149 | 151 | 157 | 163 | 167 | 173 | 179 | 181 | 191 | 193 | 197 | 199 |

73 is a prime number and can be made from the sum of two square numbers: $3^2 + 8^2 = 9 + 64 = 73$

Find ten prime numbers greater than 80 that can be made by adding two square numbers.

12 ✓ **a** Write a formula for the number of counters in the *n*th shape in the sequence in question **2**.

  b Use your formula to predict the number of counters in:

   i the tenth term   **ii** the fifteenth term.

13 Adam 'n' Even

  a Using the numbers 1 to 16 once only, can you make the totals of each of the rows, columns and diagonals in the grid even numbers?

  b Once you have found a solution, write what you notice about the number of odd and even numbers in each row and column.

  c What do you notice about the diagonals?

  d Can you find a different solution? Use what you have discovered about odd and even numbers.

14 a What is the missing number? Explain your thinking.

  b If the number on the bottom line is called *n*, can you write the number on the top line in terms of *n*?

16	32	48	12
2		6	1.5

15 Follow these instructions.

  Pick a number.
  Add 10.
  Double your answer.
  Add 40.
  Divide by 2.
  Subtract the number you began with.
  Note down your answer.
  Try some other starting numbers.
  What do you notice?
  Does it always happen?
  Why?

16 🏠 **Zip Zap!**

  Devise your own Zip Zap puzzle. Remember to use each of the digits 1 to 9 once only. Write your clues clearly and swap with a partner.

SOLVING WORD PROBLEMS

Essential Exercises

1  The sum of two square numbers is 185. What are they?

2 a Which is greater: 35% of £52 or 52% of £35?   **b** Explain your answer.

3 This chart shows the cost of buying birdseed, either in individual 1 kg packs or in large sacks.

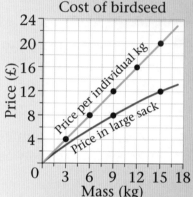

Cost of birdseed

a Estimate how much cheaper it is to buy 15 kg in a large sack rather than in fifteen 1 kg packs.

b I spent £20 on birdseed, half the weight in individual packs and half in a large sack. How much seed did I buy?

4 ✓ The product of two prime numbers is 119. What are the numbers?

5 At a car boot sale I bought six CDs for a total of £17. Some of the CDs cost £1, some cost £2 and a few cost £10. How many did I buy at each price?

Consolidation Exercises

6 In this tower, each number is the sum of the two numbers directly below it.

a What number must x stand for?

b What number must x stand for in this tower?

7  A supermarket gives reward points for the amount of money spent. Jane spends £28 and gets 35 points.

a How much money must Jane spend to earn 1 point?

b The following week she gets 55 points. How much did she spend?

c The next week she spends £45.60. How many points does she get?

8 In a game show, contestants win £20 for each correct answer but lose £10 for each wrong answer.

Look at this table.

How many questions did each contestant get right?

Clue: Think about what is the maximum a contestant can win if all their answers are correct. How much would they win if they got one wrong, two wrong, etc.?

Contestant	Number of questions	Amount won
A	14	£100
B	12	£150
C	21	£180

9 By putting different numbers in the square, triangle and circle, find five ways of completing the equation.

$$\square + \triangle + \bigcirc = 0.01$$

Challenging Exercises

10 A square and a rectangle have the same area. The sides of the rectangle are in the ratio 4:1 and its perimeter is 200 cm.

What is the length of a side of the square?

11 Dan and Ben are flatmates. Each month they pay money into a joint account to pay bills. Dan pays twice as much as Ben plus an extra £10.

a If £130 is paid into the account, how much does each pay?

b Call Ben's amount n. Can you write the amount paid into the account in terms of n?

12 I fill a cup $\frac{1}{4}$ full with lemonade and another cup twice the size $\frac{1}{2}$ full with lemonade, then top them up with water and pour them into a jug.

What proportion of the liquid is lemonade and what proportion is water?

13 🏠 A square and a rectangle have the same area. The sides of the rectangle are in the ratio 9:1 and its perimeter is 200 cm.

What is the length of a side of the square?

IDENTIFYING INFORMATION

1 At a flower show a collection of roses was arranged in a square formation. During the day 32 of the roses were sold. At the end of the day, the remaining roses were then rearranged into a smaller square.

During the second day a further eight roses were sold.

What was the original number of roses?

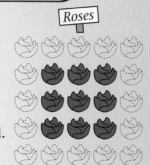

2 At the start of the school year Luke scored 2 out of 10 on his first weekly maths test.

a For the next few weeks Luke scored 10 out of 10. Copy and complete this table for the next few weeks.

	Week 1	Week 2	Week 3	Week 4	Week 5	Week 6
Total of scores	2	12				
Mean score	2					

b ✓ In which week will Luke have raised his mean score to 8?

3 At the start of the school year Li scored 4 out of 10 on her first weekly maths test.

If she scores 10 out of 10 for the next few weeks, when will she have raised her mean score to 9 or above?

4 This game involves tossing two coins at once. If both of the coins land on heads (HH) or both land on tails (TT), you win. If only one coin lands on heads, you lose.

Explain whether you are likely to win this game more times than you would lose.

5 Suppose the numbers 4 and 5 on your calculator don't work.

Find and record three ways to display each of the following numbers.

a 45   **b** 240   **c** 455   **d** 4444   **e** 5555   **f** 5454

6 Can you arrange four 9s, using any mathematical symbols you like, to equal 100?

8

7 You will need centimetre squared paper for this activity.

Copy the shape in the grid onto the centre of your squared paper.

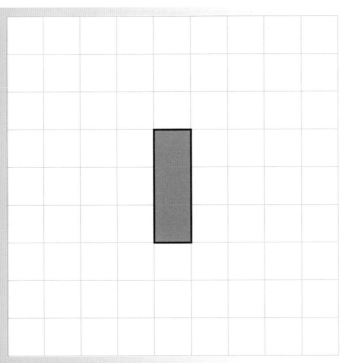

Colour it. In a different colour, shade any squares that touch the original shape along at least one side to form a frame, as in this diagram.

Change colour and shade any squares that touch the new shape along at least one side.

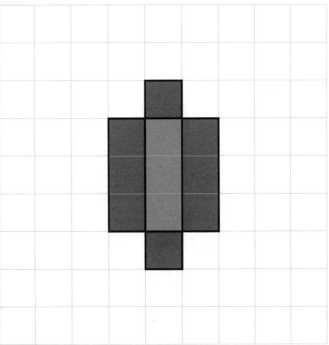

a Copy and complete the table, filling in the number of new squares in each frame as you go.

3 squares in a line

Shape	1	2	3	4	5	6
Number of new squares	8					

b Describe any patterns you notice.

8 This is an activity for three or four people. It is designed to find out who is best at estimating a period of 30 seconds.

 a Take turns to estimate 30 seconds and, each time, note how many seconds have actually passed.

 b Do this several times for each person and work out the mean estimate for each person.

 c Did some people always tend to overestimate and some underestimate?

 d Did people's estimates improve with practice?

 e Write about what you have found.

9 Look at the digits in this equation: $21 \times 48 = 84 \times 12$

The digits on one side of the equals sign have been reversed to make the numbers on the other side.

Can you find any other multiplication statements where this happens?

Clue: look at this diagram.

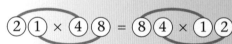

10 Now try the activity in question **7** with this starting shape.

Copy and complete the table, filling in the number of new squares as you go.

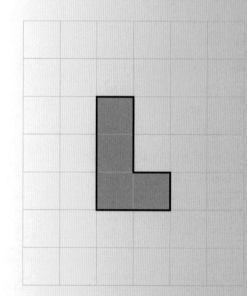

4 squares in L shape

Shape	1	2	3	4	5	6
Number of new squares	9	13				

Describe any patterns you notice.

11 This game involves tossing three coins at once. If two or three of the coins land heads up, you win. If only one coin lands heads up, you lose. Explain whether you are likely to win this game more times than you would lose.

12 Last year my age was a square number and next year it will be a cube number.

    a How old am I now?

    b In how many years' time will my age be both a square and a cube?

13 This is an activity for two people.

Instructions

Draw three dots on paper.

Player 1 draws a line that joins one dot to another, then puts another dot somewhere along the new line.

Player 2 draws another line that joins two dots, and then puts another dot somewhere along their new line.

Rules

A line must not go through any other line.

A dot can't have more than three lines coming from it.

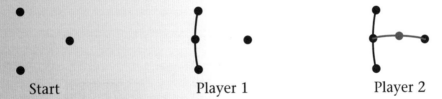

      Start   Player 1   Player 2

Take turns until someone can't go.

Play several games.

Think about these questions:

    a Is it better to go first or second?

    b What is the largest number of new lines drawn in a game?

    c What is the smallest number of new lines drawn in a game?

    d Is there a way of playing that means the games will be long?

    e Is there a way of playing that means the games will be short?

    Write a report explaining what you have found.

14 Now try the activity in question **7** on triangular paper with this starting shape.

a Copy and complete the table, filling in the number of new triangles.

Shape	1	2	3	4	5	6
Number of new triangles						

b Describe any patterns you notice.

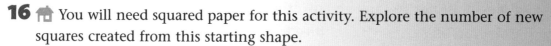

Forgotten the rules? See question 3 on page 19.

15 🏠 **Zip Zap!**

Devise your own Zip Zap puzzle. Remember to use each of the digits 1 to 9 once only. Write your clues clearly and swap with a partner.

16 🏠 You will need squared paper for this activity. Explore the number of new squares created from this starting shape.

Remember: each new square must touch a square in the original shape along at least one side. Try other starting shapes.

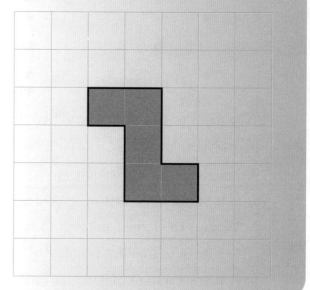

BREAKING INTO STEPS

Essential Exercises

1 You have two jugs, one holds 5 litres and the other 3 litres. Neither jug has any markings on it. You have no other containers.

Explain how you can measure out exactly 4 litres. You can refill and empty the jugs.

3 litres

5 litres

2 In Round 1 of the men's singles at Wimbledon this year there were 128 players playing 64 matches. In Round 2 there were 64 players and 32 matches and so on.

  a How many men's matches were played in the tournament in total?

  b If each match was an average of 4 sets, how many sets were played?

  c ✓ If, on average, a set contained 9 games and one game lasted for 5 minutes, how many hours of tennis were played?

3 Lucy, Emily and Alice travelled to a disco. They were wearing a skirt, a dress and a pair of trousers, but not necessarily in that order. Use these clues to find out who was wearing what.

Lucy and the girl who was wearing a skirt went by bus.

The girl in trousers said Lucy looked great.

Alice sat with the girl who was in trousers.

Consolidation Exercises

4 Rob, Jo and Ali live in a three-storey block of flats. Each flat has a different coloured door.

Jo lives in the flat with the red door.

Rob's favourite drink is coffee.

Ali doesn't drink tea.

The person whose favourite drink is tea lives on the top floor.

The flat of the person whose favourite drink is orange juice has a yellow door.

The flat with the blue door is the middle flat.

> Who drinks tea?

> Whose flat has a blue door?

> Who lives on the top floor?

Copy and complete this table.

Floor	Name	Door colour	Drink
Top			
Middle			
Bottom			

Challenging Exercises

5 ✓ How many triangles can you see in this diagram? Make sure you count all the triangles of any size.

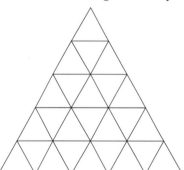

6 How many triangles can you see in this diagram? Make sure you count all the triangles of any size.

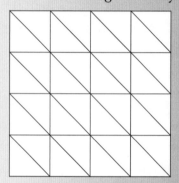

7 🖩 The letters s, k and y represent single-digit numbers and $s^y \times k^k = sky$. What numbers do s, k and y stand for?

8 Yellow wooden rods are 2 cm long. Green wooden rods are 7 cm long.

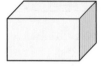 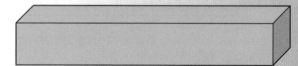

They can be joined end-to-end to make one length.

a Using as many yellow and/or green rods as you need, what different lengths can you make?

For example: 16 → yellow + green + green or 16 = 2 + 7 + 7.

b Which lengths less than 10 cm are impossible to make?

c Explain why you can be certain that every integer length above 5 cm is possible.

ESTABLISHING SOLUTIONS

Essential Exercises

1 This is an activity for two people. Put a pile of counters on the table. (Alternatively, write a number, e.g. 23, to represent the counters and subtract from that.)

Take turns to subtract 1, 2 or 3 counters from the pile. The person who has to take the last counter loses the game.

a Play several times, recording each move.

b Can you devise a strategy that will win the game?

Counters left	Counters taken	
	Me	Partner
23	1	
22		3
19	2	
17		

2 The number 24 has eight factors: 1, 2, 3, 4, 6, 8, 12 and 24. Six of these are even numbers and two are odd.

a Find all the numbers between 1 and 40 whose factors, apart from 1, are all even.

b What is the difference between each of the numbers? What do you notice?

c Describe the sequence of these numbers in words.

3 Dan says:

> It's possible to use each of the digits from 1 to 9 once only in the boxes to make the number sentence correct. Can you do it?

The digits 2, 4, 6 and 8 have been filled in to help you.

$$\boxed{6} \times \boxed{2}\,\boxed{} = \boxed{}\,\boxed{}\,\boxed{4} = \boxed{} \times \boxed{}\,\boxed{8}$$

4 ✓ Sam has a box of CDs. When asked how many she has she replies, 'Two-thirds of one-quarter of my CDs is 12.' How many CDs has she got?

5 Knight's moves

In a game of chess a knight moves two squares vertically and one square horizontally or two squares horizontally and one square vertically. Some of the possible moves are shown here.

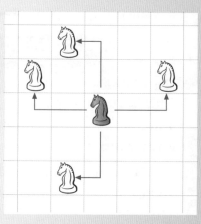

a Draw a 5 × 5 grid and mark all eight possible knight's moves from the centre square.

b Draw a 3 × 3 grid. Write '1' anywhere in the grid. Use a knight's move to move to another square. Write '2' there.

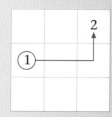

Continue to use knight's moves and the numbers 3, 4, etc. How many of the squares can you fill with a number before you can't move any further?

c ✓ Do this several times. What is the maximum number of squares you can fill?

d Try knight's moves on a 4 × 4 grid. Is it possible to fill all the squares? What is the maximum number you can fill?

Consolidation Exercises

6 The number 8 has four factors: 1, 2, 4 and 8. Three of these are even and one is odd.

a Find all the numbers between 1 and 20 that have half their factors even.

b Describe the sequence these numbers make.

c Can you describe the sequence in terms of n?

7 Write out the first 12 square numbers.

a Find the digital root of each square number.

b What do you notice about the digital roots?

> Find the digital root of a number by adding the digits in the number until you reach a single digit, like this .... 54 → 9.

Teacher:

c Can you see a pattern that would allow you to predict the digital roots of further squares?

d Could you use this to predict what these further squares might be?

e Continue the list of squares using this method and then check your list with a calculator.

8 Adam says:

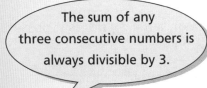

> The sum of any three consecutive numbers is always divisible by 3.

Is Adam right?

a Let *n* stand for the middle number of the three. Write the other two numbers in terms of *n*. Find the sum of the three and use this to help you explain why Adam's statement is true.

b Now try five consecutive numbers. Can you make a statement like Adam's?

c Investigate other sets of consecutive numbers in a similar way. Use *n* to stand for a number to help you explain your reasoning.

9 Can you find a three-digit number that satisfies both these conditions:

  i each digit in the number is a prime number

  ii each digit divides exactly into the three-digit number.

10 This arrangement of numbers is known as Pascal's triangle. Explore the arrangement and copy and continue it for several more rows. Write down any patterns you notice in it.

Look at the numbers in the diagonal rows.

Look at the total of each row. What do you notice?

```
          1
        1   1
      1   2   1
    1   3   3   1
  1   4   6   4   1
  _   _   _   _   _   _
```

11 A designer is given this problem.

> Make a box with the greatest volume possible if the total of the length, width and height is 1 m.

a What is the largest volume you can find? Remember that the volume of a cuboid is found by multiplying the length by the width by the height.

b The designer's finished box did not quite have the greatest possible volume. It was a square prism with a volume of $36\,288\,cm^3$. What were his dimensions?

12 a Try knight's moves on a 5×5 grid. Is it possible to fill all the squares? Can you fill more than 20?

b What if you try a 6×6 grid?

13 Here is an 8×8 square containing the numbers 1 to 64.

a Can you use knight's moves to travel through the grid from 1 to 64?

b Find the totals of 3 rows or columns. What do you notice?

c Is it true for all rows and columns?

d What do you notice about the sums of half of each row and column?

1	48	31	50	33	16	63	18
30	51	46	3	62	19	14	35
47	2	49	32	15	34	17	64
52	29	4	45	20	61	36	13
5	44	25	56	9	40	21	60
28	53	8	41	24	57	12	37
43	6	55	26	39	10	59	22
54	27	42	7	58	23	38	11

Challenging Exercises

14 It is known that a fake £2 coin has been mixed with 26 real £2 coins. The fake coin looks identical but is 2 grams heavier. Using a pair of balance scales, what is the smallest number of weighings needed to find the fake?

15 a Look at the table. For all the rows, the rule to explain how the number in the last column is made is: A + B − C. Work out the missing number.

A	B	C	Answer
3	6	8	1
7	8	5	10
3	7	12	−2
7	20	3	

b Work out the rule for the this table and copy and complete it.

A	B	C	Answer
2	5	8	2
1	6	5	1
10	10	6	94
5	3	9	

16 a What other patterns do you notice in the grid in question **13**?

b What do you notice about the numbers in the grey and white squares?

17

> The difference between the squares of two consecutive numbers will always be an odd number.

Sarah:

Is this true? Can you prove it?

Clue: call the consecutive numbers *n* and *n* + 1.

18 Write a report on the investigations you have done.

INVESTIGATING AND GENERALISING

Essential Exercises

1 Draw four dots with no more than two in a straight line.

   a How many straight lines are needed to join each dot to every other dot?

   b Explore other arrangements of four dots. Is the answer always the same?

   c Explore other numbers of dots, e.g. 3 dots, 5 dots, 6 dots. Is there a pattern? Describe the pattern in words.

   d Can you predict how many lines will be needed to join 7 dots, 9 dots or 10 dots?

2 How many 1 cm × 1 cm squares will be in the twelfth diagram?

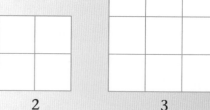

Diagram   1   2   3

Consolidation Exercises

3 ✓ **a** Describe the pattern in question **2** in terms of n.

   b How many squares will be in the thirtieth diagram?

4 a How many dots will be needed for the fifth pattern in this sequence?

   b How many will be needed for the nth pattern?

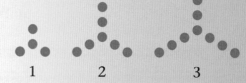

1   2   3

5 There are three streets in a small village. Each street is straight and there is a postbox at each crossroads. Think about how the streets might be arranged.

   a What is the greatest number of postboxes that could be needed?

   b What if there were four streets?   **c** What if there were five streets?

   d What if there were six streets?   **e** Draw a table to show your results.

   f Describe any patterns you notice.

6 🏠 There are 32 teams in the first round of a football tournament. The winners of each match go through to the next round.

   a How many matches were played in the tournament in total?

   b What do you notice about this number?

   c How many matches do you think will be played in a tournament with 64 teams?

   d How many matches would be played in a tournament with 256 teams?

7 Solve this Zip Zap puzzle. Forgotten the rules? See question **3** on page 19.

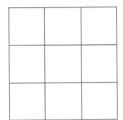

Tip: If you're not sure of all the digits in a Zip or Zap, just write in the digits you're sure of.

Across

Zap 1   has a units digit that is the product of the other two digits.

Zap 2   is made up of 3 odd digits with a sum of 17.

Zap 3   includes a hundreds digit of 3, and is divisible by 15.

Down

Zip 1   is an odd number, where the sum of 2 of the digits is equal to the third.

Zip 2   is even and the sum of the digits is 17.

Zip 3   is 900 when rounded to the nearest 100 and also when rounded to the nearest 10.

Challenging Exercises

8 You will need some dotted paper.

   a On a 4×4 grid, carefully draw several simple polygons and find the area of each, A.

   b Now find the number of dots inside each shape, i, and the number of boundary dots, b. In the shape shown $A = 8$, $i = 4$ and $b = 10$. Write your results in a table.

   c Devise a formula, expressed in terms of A, i and b, that will show the relationship between the area, the number of dots inside the shape and the number of boundary dots of any polygon.

Remember: a polygon is a 2D shape with straight sides.

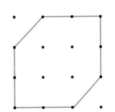

SOLVING WORD PROBLEMS

Essential Exercises

1 ✓ Jack was mixing mortar using sand and cement. Into the mixer he put three times more sand than cement and added an extra 4 kg of sand. In total he made 28 kg of mortar.

How much sand did he use?

2 🔲 A 380 g box of breakfast cereal costs £1.52. How much is this per 100 g?

3 🔲 A garden centre sells bags of grass seed in three sizes.

a Which bag is the best value for money?

b How much is the seed per kg in this bag?

> **GRASS SEED**
> £5.70 for 4.5 kg
> £7.50 for 6 kg
> £9.60 for 8 kg

4 🔲 Jo and Anna each bought a copy of the same video from the same shop. Jo bought hers when there was 16% off the original price. Anna bought hers the following day when there was 30% off. Jo's video cost £1.75 more than Anna's. What was the original price of the video?

5 🔲 This pie chart shows how pupils in class 9B get to school.

Four pupils walk to school.

How many pupils come by bus?

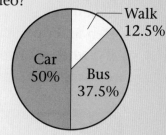

6 🔲 Packs of blank cassettes come in two sizes: £4.20 for 5 and £6.64 for 8.

a Which size is better value for money?   **b** By how much?

7 What fraction is halfway between:

a $\frac{5}{6}$ and $\frac{7}{8}$ **b** $\frac{3}{7}$ and $\frac{5}{9}$ **c** $\frac{3}{7}$ and $\frac{3}{11}$?

8 The opposite faces of a normal dice add up to 7. Each of these shapes can be folded to make a dice.

Mark in the missing numbers to create three normal dice.

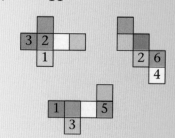

9 The price of a box of chocolates is £8.00. The pie chart shows what proportion of the price is for transport, labour, ingredients and profit.

What is the amount of profit on this box of chocolates?

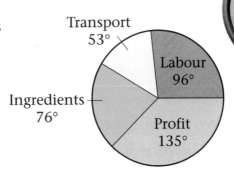

Transport 53°

Labour 96°

Ingredients 76°

Profit 135°

10 A supermarket gives bonus points for the amount of money spent. Luke spends £27 and gets 45 points.

a The following week he gets 54 points. How much did he spend?

b The next week he spends £46.20. How many points does he get?

11 ✓ The product of two prime numbers is 253. What are the numbers?

12 These are Serena's test scores over three weeks.

a In which test did she do best?

b Write each score as a percentage to two decimal places.

Test Marks	
Week 1	9/17
Week 2	5/9
Week 3	15/28

13 Try these on your calculator.

$1 \times 1 = 1$

$11 \times 11 =$

$111 \times 111 =$

$1111 \times 1111 =$

a Can you predict the answers to the next three calculations in this pattern?

b Can you predict the answers to further questions?

c Why do you think this happens? Use and continue these diagrams to help you explain your thinking.

11×11

x	10	1
10	100	10
1	10	1 = 121

111×111

x	100	10	1
100	10000	100	
10			
1			

1111×1111

x	1000	100	10	1
1000				
100				
10				
1				

14 Try these on your calculator. $9 \times 9 \quad =$

$99 \times 99 \quad =$

$999 \times 999 =$

a Can you predict the answers to the next three calculations in this pattern?

b What do you notice? Explain why you think this happens. Use diagrams like those in question **13** to help you explain your thinking.

c Try this again, this time using the number 5.

d Can you predict the answers to further questions? Explain.

Consolidation Exercises

15 In this tower, each number is the sum of the two numbers directly below it.

a What number must *a* stand for?

b What number must *a* stand for in this tower?

16 Find five ways of completing this equation by writing a fraction or mixed number in each shape. $\square - \triangle - \bigcirc = \frac{3}{4}$

17 This graph shows the number of pets owned by people in a survey. Unfortunately Lee has spilt his drink over part of it.

Let *n* be the number of people with three pets.

a Show that the total number of pets owned by the people in the survey is $34 + 3n$.

b Write an expression for the total number of people.

c If the total number of pets is 58, what is the value of *n*?

d How many people were surveyed?

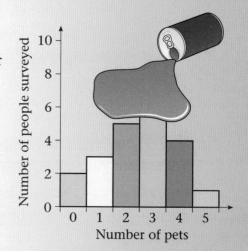

18 A shop has two shelves for pots of jam. Each shelf has the same number of pots on it.

The probability of picking a pot of strawberry jam at random from the first shelf is $\frac{1}{5}$.

The probability of picking a pot of strawberry jam at random from the second shelf is $\frac{1}{2}$.

If all the pots are placed on a new, larger shelf, what is the probability of picking a pot of strawberry jam at random?

19 a Try these on your calculator.

$$6 \times 88 \quad =$$
$$6 \times 888 \quad =$$
$$6 \times 8888 \quad =$$

b What do you notice?

c Can you predict the answers to further calculations? Explain.

d Explore 6×99, 6×999 in the same way.

e Describe what you find. Can you explain why you think this happens?

f Can you predict the answers to further calculations?

20 Investigate 8×99, 8×999, ...

Write a report saying what you noticed and why this happens. Can you find a rule that will allow you to predict answers to similar questions?

Challenging Exercises

21 There are two crates of roof tiles in a builder's yard.

Each crate contains the same number of tiles.

The probability of picking a grey tile at random from the first crate is $\frac{1}{4}$.

The probability of picking a grey tile at random from the second crate is $\frac{1}{3}$.

a If all the tiles are put together, what is the probability of picking a grey tile at random?

b What would the probability be of picking a grey tile at random if the first crate contained twice as many tiles as the second crate?

22 Vijay finished the 5000 m race in 22 min 19.6 s.

    a What was his average speed in m/s?

  b What would it be sensible to round the answer to?

  c Rhian cycled 12 000 m in 50 min 12.4 s. What was her average speed?

23 A cylinder is 8.4 cm tall and has a circumference of 20.4 cm.

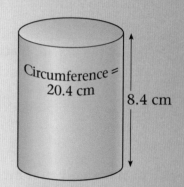

Circumference = 20.4 cm

8.4 cm

    a What is its volume?

    b Find three other cylinders with a volume between 200 cm³ and 300 cm³. Try to make them as close to your first answer as possible. Which of your three cylinders has the largest surface area?

24 a Find the length of AB.

    b Explain your method.

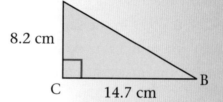

8.2 cm

A

C   14.7 cm   B

    c Is the blue triangle a right-angled triangle?

    d Explain how you know this.

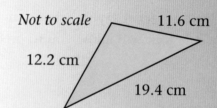

Not to scale   11.6 cm

12.2 cm

19.4 cm

25 The diagram shows two identical place mats on a circular table.

What percentage of the table is covered by the mats?

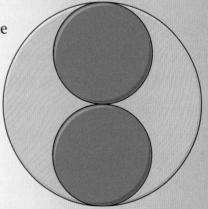

IDENTIFYING INFORMATION

1 At a flower show a collection of roses was arranged in a square formation. During the day 100 of the roses were sold. At the end of the day, the remaining roses were then rearranged into a smaller square. What was the original number of roses?

2 The sum of the ages of a brother and sister is 20. In two years' time the brother will be three times as old as the sister. How old is the sister now?

Consolidation Exercises

3 You will need centimetre squared paper for this activity.

a Colour one square in the centre of your squared paper.

b In a different colour, shade any squares that touch the original shape along one side only to form a frame, like this.

c Change colour and shade any squares that touch the new shape along one side only.

d Continue in this way, colouring only squares that touch each shape along one side only.

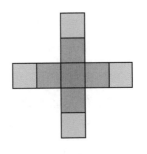

e Copy and complete the table, filling in the number of new squares in each frame and then the total squares.

Shape	1	2	3	4	5	6	7	8	9	10	11	12
Number of new squares	1	4	4									
Total number of squares	1	5	9									

Explain what you have done and describe any patterns you notice.

4 Lynford made a 3 × 3 × 3 cube from small white cubes.

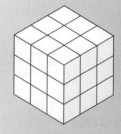

He dipped it into blue paint, let it dry and then took it apart.

a Write down how many of the small cubes had no blue faces, 1 blue face, 2 blue faces and so on.

b Now try this for a 4 × 4 × 4 cube.

5 ✓ The sum of the ages of a father and daughter is 52. In four years' time the father will be four times as old as the daughter. How old is the daughter now?

6 The area of this lawn is $36\,\text{m}^2$.

Work out the value of x and then find the perimeter of the lawn.

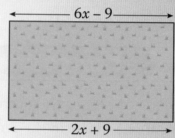

Challenging Exercises

7 In seven years' time Jo's mother will be twice as old as Jo. In thirteen years' time the sum of their ages will be 75. How old are they now?

8 Solve this Zip Zap puzzle. Forgotten the rules?

See question **3** on page 19.

> **Tip:** If you're not sure of all the digits in a Zip or Zap, just write in the digits you're sure of.

Across

Zap 1 is a multiple of 9, 600 < Zap 1 < 640.
Zap 2 is even and has a digital root of 7.
Zap 3 includes the digits 8, 3 and 9.

Down

Zip 1 is an odd number, exactly divisible by 7, and the sum of its digits is 22.
Zip 2 is odd and is a multiple of both 3 and 17.
Zip 3 is 200 when rounded to the nearest 100 and 250 when rounded to the nearest 10.

BREAKING INTO STEPS

Essential Exercises

1 Choose a two-digit number, for example 25.
Square each of the digits and add them together.
Now square each of the digits of your new number.
Continue until you reach a single-digit number.

a Try this with your own two-digit number.
Which single-digit number did you reach?

b Do this many times, noting which two-digit numbers end with which
single digit numbers.

c You might choose to record your findings as chains of numbers. Write a
report explaining any patterns you find.

2 The grids show six different views of the cube which is made up
of 8 smaller cubes.

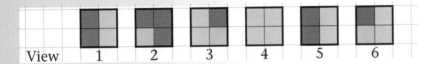

Can you build a 2 × 2 × 2 cube from blue, red and green cubes which, when
turned, can match each of the six views?

Consolidation Exercises

3 ✓ **a** Jack and Molly each have a
sum of money.

> If you gave me £1, I will
> have twice as much as you, but,
> instead, if I give you £1 we will
> have the same.

Jack:

Explain how much money they
each have.

b Today they have different
amounts of money.

> If I give you £1 you will
> have half my amount but, instead,
> if you give me £1, I will have five
> times as much as you.

Molly:

Explain how much money they
each have.

4 You will need squared or dotted paper for this activity. The diagrams show ways of splitting a 4 × 4 grid into 16, 4 and 8 squares.

1	2	3	4
5	6	7	8
9	10	11	12
13	14	15	16

1		2	
3		4	

			2
1			3
			4
8	7	6	5

How many ways of splitting a 4 × 4 grid into different numbers of squares can you find?

5 Robin has bought some chickens. He has 20 m of chicken wire to create a living area for them. What is the largest possible area he could create?

6 a 🖩 What are the dimensions of a cube that has a surface area of approximately 1 m²? Give your answers in centimetres to two decimal places.

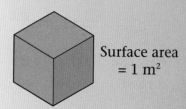

Surface area = 1 m²

b What is its volume in cm³?

7 These grids show six different views of a different shape. Only **six** small cubes were used to build it.

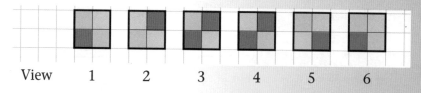

View   1   2   3   4   5   6

Can you join six small blue, red and green cubes to match each of the six views?

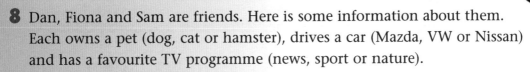
8 Dan, Fiona and Sam are friends. Here is some information about them.
Each owns a pet (dog, cat or hamster), drives a car (Mazda, VW or Nissan)
and has a favourite TV programme (news, sport or nature).

Also:

– Dan's favourite programmes are about nature.
– The person who likes sport has a hamster.
– Sam doesn't like sport.
– The cat owner does not have a Mazda.
– The Mazda owner does not like sport programmes.
– The person who watches nature programmes does not have a cat.
– The cat owner does not have a VW.

> Who watches sport?

> Who owns the Mazda?

> Who has a dog?

Copy and complete this table:

Name	Type of car	TV programme	Pet

9 Jack and Molly each have a sum of money.

> If you give me £1 I will have seven times as much as you, but, instead, if I give you £1 I will have the same as you started with.

Explain how much money they each have.

Molly:

Clue: in this question the sums of money
are not whole pounds.

10 Here are six different views of another shape made up of small cubes.

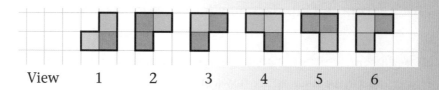

View 1 2 3 4 5 6

Can you join cubes together to match each of the six views?

11 Make up your own shape, draw the six views and swap with a partner. Can you solve each other's?

12 Now try to construct this cube, made from 27 smaller cubes.

Can you connect cubes together to match each of the six views?

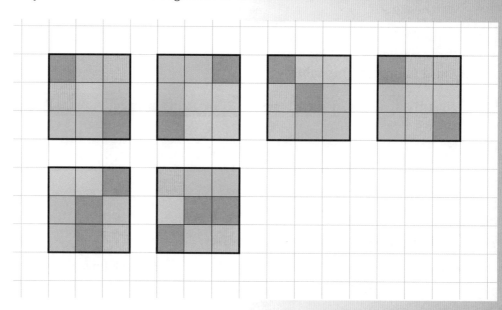

ESTABLISHING SOLUTIONS 1

Essential Exercises

1. This sequence of numbers is called the Fibonacci sequence.

   1   1   2   3   5   8   13

   a ✓ Can you see how the sequence is generated?
   b Continue the sequence until you reach a number over 2000.
   c Find the difference between adjacent numbers in the sequence. What do you notice?
   d List any square numbers in the sequence.
   e List any cube numbers in the sequence.
   f Write the first five prime numbers in the sequence.
   g Find a multiple of 9 in your sequence.
   h Continue the sequence to find the next multiple of 9.

2. The number 24 has eight factors: 1, 2, 3, 4, 6, 8, 12 and 24. Six of these are even numbers and two are odd.

   a Find numbers between 1 and 40 whose factors, apart from 1, are all even.
   b What is the difference between each of the numbers? What do you notice?
   c Can you describe the sequence in terms of n?

3. a Cut out a 15 × 15 square from centimetre-squared paper.

   b Cut one square centimetre from each corner.

   c Fold up the sides to make an open box.

   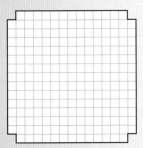

   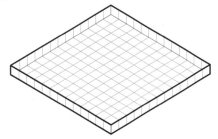

   d Without going above the level of the top of the sides, how much can the box hold?

e Cut further squares from the corners. What are the dimensions of the box with the greatest capacity?

Record your results in a table.

Size of corner cut-outs	Dimensions of tray			Capacity cm³
	l	w	h	
1 × 1	13	13	1	169
2 × 2				
3 × 3				
4 × 4				

f Use your calculator to try to increase the maximum possible capacity.

4 You will need 3 × 3 dotted paper for this activity. It is possible to draw eight different triangles using 3 × 3 grids. Be careful to avoid translations, rotations and reflections. Can you find all eight?

Consolidation Exercises

5 a Find the sum of the first seven numbers in the Fibonacci sequence.

b Find the sum of the first eight numbers.

c Find the sum of the first nine numbers.

d Compare your answers with the ninth, tenth and eleventh numbers in the sequence. What do you notice?

e Use this information to find the total of the first 16 numbers in the sequence, without adding them. Explain how you worked out this answer.

6 This pattern of squares, fitted together to make rectangles, has been made using the numbers in the Fibonacci sequence. Each new square added in the pattern has sides that are the length of the next number in the sequence.

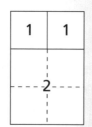

Copy these first few shapes and continue the pattern. Is it always possible to make a rectangle? Can you explain your thinking?

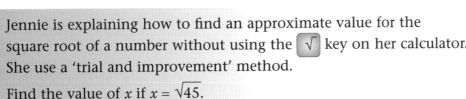

7 Jennie is explaining how to find an approximate value for the square root of a number without using the $\sqrt{}$ key on her calculator. She use a 'trial and improvement' method.

Find the value of x if $x = \sqrt{45}$.

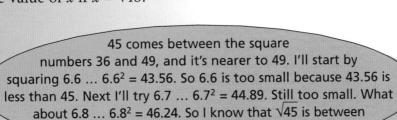

> 45 comes between the square numbers 36 and 49, and it's nearer to 49. I'll start by squaring 6.6 ... $6.6^2 = 43.56$. So 6.6 is too small because 43.56 is less than 45. Next I'll try 6.7 ... $6.7^2 = 44.89$. Still too small. What about 6.8 ... $6.8^2 = 46.24$. So I know that $\sqrt{45}$ is between 6.7 and 6.8. What about 6.71...?

Jennie:

Use Jennie's method to find the square roots of these numbers, correct to two decimal places. Show your working.

a 39   **b** 53   **c** 92

8 Using four 4s each time and any mathematical symbols you like, how many of the numbers from 0 to 10 can you make?

For example: $0 = 44 - 44$

9 Can you make the numbers from 11 to 20 using four 4s? You're allowed to use 4 squared for these, like this: $4^2 + 4 - \dfrac{4}{4}$

10 a Find two cube numbers each made from the same digits.

b Are there any other two- or three-digit cube numbers for which this is true?

11 Ben is shopping for some T-shirts. The assistant says, 'You can have four T-shirts and £3 change or three T-shirts and £8 change.'

a Make and solve an equation using the two expressions.

b How much is a T-shirt?

12 Ben meets the same assistant in the sports department. He says, 'You can have six tennis balls and have £3 change or four with £6 change.' How much is one ball?

13 You will need 4 × 4 dotted paper for this activity.

How many different quadrilaterals can you draw using a 4 × 4 grid? You can have more than one of each type of quadrilateral as long as you avoid translations, rotations and reflections.

a Name each of your shapes.

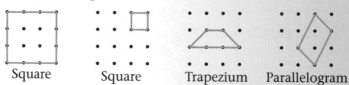

Square   Square   Trapezium   Parallelogram

b When you have over 25, check with a friend and add to your collection.

Keep your sheet for a later question in the Challenging Exercises section.

Challenging Exercises

14 This pattern is made from pairs of adjacent numbers in the Fibonacci sequence. The larger number is written as the numerator, the smaller as the denominator. Continue this pattern by dividing the numerator by the denominator. Round answers to 3 or 4 decimal places if necessary.

$$\frac{2}{1} = \qquad\qquad \frac{3}{2} = \qquad\qquad \frac{5}{3} =$$

$$\frac{8}{5} = \qquad\qquad \frac{13}{8} = \qquad\qquad \frac{21}{13} =$$

Continue until you reach the last numbers in your sequence.

Write what you notice about your answers.

15 If the Fibonacci sequence is continued the adjacent numbers 317 811 and 514 229 are reached.

a Divide the larger number by the smaller number. Write the answer shown on the calculator in full. When looking at this pattern as part of ratios and rectangles Ancient Greek mathematicians called this number the golden number.

b Square this golden number and write the answer in full.

c What do you notice about this answer?

16 🖩

> When you multiply a number by its reciprocal the answer is 1: $\frac{1}{2}$ is the reciprocal of 2.

a Find the reciprocal of the golden number, in question **15**.

b What do you notice about the reciprocal?

17 🖩 Using two integers chosen from between 0 and 50 find a fraction that is as close to the golden number as you can find.

18 🏠 Design a poster about some of the patterns you discovered about Fibonacci and the golden ratio. Find out more information about this from the internet or from books.

19 Use Jennie's method in question **7** to find approximate values for x for these cube root equations.

   a $x = \sqrt[3]{47}$ **b** $x = \sqrt[3]{62}$ **c** $x^3 = 98$

20 This diagram shows two identical circles that overlap.

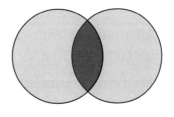

   a The red region has an area that is 25% of the area of one circle. What percentage of the whole shape is the red region?

   b If the red region had an area that is 32% of the area of one circle, what percentage of the whole shape would the red region be?

21 You will need the set of quadrilaterals from question **13**. Which of your quadrilaterals have diagonals that:

   a are at right angles   **b** are of equal length   **c** bisect each other?

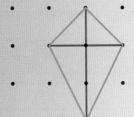 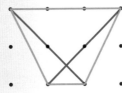  

ESTABLISHING SOLUTIONS 2

Essential Exercises

1 ✓**a** Look at this table. For all the rows, the rule to explain how the number in the last column is made is

$\frac{1}{2}A + B - C.$

Work out the missing number.

A	B	C	Answer
8	6	8	2
10	8	1	12
1	7	2	$5\frac{1}{2}$
5	12	3	

Work out the rule for these tables and copy and complete them.

b

A	B	C	Answer
2	5	8	1
1	6	5	3
10	10	6	24
5	3	9	

c

A	B	C	Answer
2	5	10	52
1	6	5	31
9	3	7	30
20	8	5	

2 This is an activity for two people. Put 31 counters on the table. (Alternatively, write the number 31 on paper to represent the counters and subtract from that.)

Take turns to subtract 1, 2, 3, 4 or 5 counters from the pile. The person who has to take the last counter loses the game.

Play several times, recording each move.

Can you devise a strategy that will win the game?

3 Each of these containers fills at a constant rate. Draw a graph for each bottle showing the depth of liquid against time.

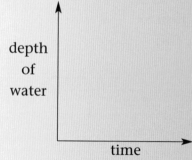

4 Work out the rules for each of these tables and copy and complete them. Each number is used only once in any order, but numbers can be halved or doubled and any operation can be used.

a

A	B	C	Answer
8	6	8	10
10	8	1	$17\frac{1}{2}$
1	7	2	7
5	12	3	

b

A	B	C	Answer
50	5	18	22
24	6	5	7
10	10	6	−16
5	3	9	

c

A	B	C	Answer
8	11	19	22
50	8	1	−41
1	7	32	38
20	12	3	

d

A	B	C	Answer
5	5	20	95
24	6	5	6
10	10	6	50
5	3	9	

e

A	B	C	Answer
9	1	3	4
10	10	2	15
21	7	7	10
15	12	5	

f

A	B	C	Answer
1	5	3	7
2	6	20	4
5	5	6	44
5	3	9	

5 This pattern shows the number 36 divided by numbers getting closer and closer to zero and then by numbers on the other side of zero getting progressively further away from zero. Continue the pattern.

$$36 \div 0.1 = 360$$
$$36 \div 0.01 =$$
$$36 \div 0.001 =$$
$$36 \div 0.0001 =$$
$$36 \div 0.00001 =$$
$$36 \div 0.000001 =$$
$$36 \div 0.0000001 =$$
$$36 \div 0.00000001 =$$
$$36 \div -0.00000001 =$$
$$36 \div -0.0000001 =$$
$$36 \div -0.000001 =$$
$$36 \div -0.00001 =$$
$$36 \div -0.0001 =$$
$$36 \div -0.001 =$$
$$36 \div -0.01 =$$
$$36 \div -0.1 =$$

a Look carefully at what is happening to the answers as you divide by numbers increasingly close to zero. What then happens as you cross zero and divide by numbers that become increasingly far from zero?

b Can you use this information to explain why dividing by zero is meaningless?

6 Each of these containers fills at a constant rate. Draw a graph for each bottle showing the depth of liquid against time.

a  **b**  **c**   **d**

7 📱 The diagrams show aerial views of three housing estates.

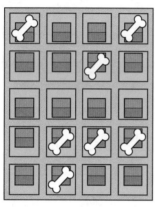

Estate 1

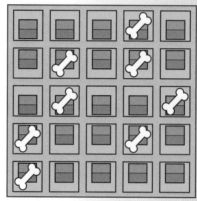

Estate 2

Estate 3

A picture of a bone means a household owns a dog.

a On which estate is the postman most likely to meet a dog?

b On which of these estates is the postman most likely to meet a dog?

    A 15 dogs in 7 rows of 5 houses   **B** 14 dogs in 8 rows of 4 houses

    C 18 dogs in 6 rows of 7 houses   **D** 78 dogs in 15 rows of 12 houses

8 A 1 cm cube has a volume of 1 cm³ and a surface area of 6 cm². A 2 cm cube has a volume of 8 cm³ and a surface area of 24 cm².

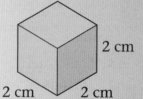

$V = 2 \times 2 \times 2 = 8 \text{ cm}^3$

Area of one face $= 2 \times 2 = 4 \text{ cm}^2$

Surface area of cube $= 6 \times 4 = 24 \text{ cm}^2$

    a Explore the relationship between surface area and volume for cubes up to 12×12. Record your results in a table and then graph them.

b Can you use what you have found to explain why some whales, which live in cold waters around the Antarctic, migrate to the warmer waters of the Caribbean to give birth?

c Can you think of any other applications of your findings?

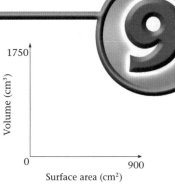

Challenging Exercises

9 a Which of these is the correct rule for this table?

$2A + B + C$　　　$A \times B \times C$

$(\frac{1}{2}A + B) \times C$　　$2C \div B \times \frac{1}{2}A$

b Find the missing number.

A	B	C	Answer
2	1	5	10
6	4	8	12
5	7	7	5
10	6	9	

10 Solve these in the same way.

a

A	B	C	Answer
6	7	35	8
10	4	28	12
1	20	100	$5\frac{1}{2}$
8	3	9	

b

A	B	C	Answer
1	5	10	120
10	1	3	66
2	−1	5	10
1	1	13	

c

A	B	C	Answer
6	8	2	48
3	6	4	36
10	7	1	35
6	3	9	

d

A	B	C	Answer
1	5	10	55
10	1	3	13
2	−2	5	−14
−2	8	4	

e

A	B	C	Answer
102	45	17	51
64	36	16	40
8	17	2	21
72	3	18	

f

A	B	C	Answer
14	5	26	8
10	5	15	5
100	6	20	20
27	20	73	

12 🏠 Write some tables of your own for others to solve. Write the rule for each table and the missing numbers and keep them separate.

INVESTIGATING AND GENERALISING

1 a Choose three consecutive numbers from this grid.

b Add them and divide the answer by 3. What do you notice about the answer?

Do this several times with different sets of three consecutive numbers.

c Explain any patterns you notice.

d Call your middle number n. Describe the other two numbers in terms of n and find the total of the three numbers.

1	2	3	4	5	6
7	8	9	10	11	12
13	14	15	16	17	18
19	20	21	22	23	24
25	26	27	28	29	30
31	32	33	34	35	36

e Can you explain why, when you divide by 3, you get the middle number?

f Try three adjacent numbers in a vertical line from the grid. Can you explain your results in terms of n?

2 a Draw a number square or rectangle like one of these. Add the numbers in opposite corners.

1	2	3
4	5	6
7	8	9

1	2	3	4
5	6	7	8
9	10	11	12
13	14	15	16

b What do you notice?

c Does it always work?

d What about other pairs of opposite numbers?

e Write a report explaining what you have found.

1	2	3	4
5	6	7	8

3 Adding two numbers and then squaring the total gives the same result as squaring two numbers and then adding them. Explain whether this is never, sometimes or always true.

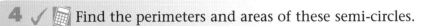

4 ✓ 🖩 Find the perimeters and areas of these semi-circles.

a
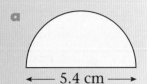
⟵ 5.4 cm ⟶

b
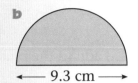
⟵ 9.3 cm ⟶

c
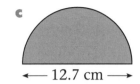
⟵ 12.7 cm ⟶

5 Jack made a flowerbed in his garden from two quarter-circles.

Find its perimeter and area.

5 m

6 🖩 This is an aerial view of another of Jack's flowerbeds made up of two equal semicircles.

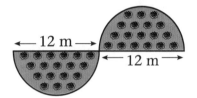
⟵ 12 m ⟶
⟵ 12 m ⟶

  a What is the perimeter of the bed?

  b What is the area of the bed?

7 Look at the diagram.

Find the area of the shaded parts of the square.

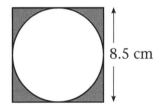
8.5 cm

Consolidation Exercises

8 Pick a number between 8 and 29 inclusive from the grid in question **1**.

Start with this number and add to it all the eight numbers that surround it in the grid, as in the diagram.

Divide your total by 9.

2	3	4
8	9	10
14	15	16

  a What number do you get?

  b Do this several times with different start numbers. Does it still work? Can you explain why?

  c Call your chosen number *n*. Describe all the surrounding numbers in terms of *n* and find the total.

9 a Pick two adjacent numbers between 8 and 29 inclusive from the grid in question **1**. For example you might pick 9 and 10 or 20 and 26.

Start with these numbers and add to them all the ten numbers that surround them in the grid.

b Divide your total by 12.

c What number do you get?

d Do this several times with different pairs of adjacent start numbers. What do you notice?

e Can you explain what you have discovered in terms of *n*?

10 Draw a multiplication square like one of these.

Multiply the numbers in opposite corners.

3	6	9
4	8	12
5	10	15

a What do you notice?

b Does it always work?

c What about other pairs of opposite numbers?

d Write a report explaining what you have found.

e Prove that in all squares like this the products of the numbers in opposite corners are the same.

f Investigate other sizes of squares and rectangles.

11 ✓ If the sum of two numbers is 15, what is the largest product they can have? (The numbers do not have to be whole numbers.)

12 Look at the diagram.

a Find the area of the shaded parts of the square.

b What percentage of the whole square is this?

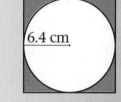

6.4 cm

13 This picture shows a circular tablecloth on a square table which has sides of 1.5 m.

a What area of the table surface is visible?

b What percentage of the whole table is this?

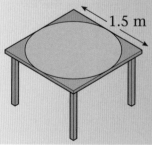

1.5 m

14 If $0 < x < 1$ and $0 < y < 1$ write what you know about the following questions:

   a $x + y$ **b** $x \times y$ **c** x^2 **d** $x - y$

   e $4y$ **f** $(x \times y)^2$ **g** $(x + y)^2$

   h   Choose other number ranges for x and y. Pose and answer similar questions.

15   If the sum of three numbers is 15, what is the largest product they could have?

16   Look at the diagram.

Find the area of one of the shaded parts of the square.

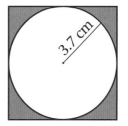

3.7 cm

17   Jack's garden has a circular flower bed inside a circular lawn.

What is the area of the lawn?

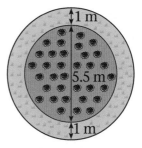

1 m

5.5 m

1 m

18 A frog is sitting on the edge of a circular lawn of radius 10 m. He intends to reach the centre of the lawn. His first jump takes him halfway towards the centre. Each subsequent jump takes him half the remaining distance. Investigate how far he has travelled after each jump. How many jumps will be needed to reach the centre?

ANSWERS TO SELF-CHECK QUESTIONS

YEAR 7

Solving word problems

Money and percentages

9   60p

Number and algebra

8a   11
b   17
c   29
d   14

Ratio and proportion

8a $35l$
b $25l$
c $15l$

Measures

3   18p

Handling data and probability

1f $\frac{1}{2}$

Breaking into steps

7   LHS 16 kg of weights RHS potatoes + 2 kg weight
11a   27 (16 + 7 + 3 + 1)
b   38

Presenting and interpreting solutions

3a   4, 5, 9, 14, 23
b $3, 7\frac{1}{2}, 10\frac{1}{2}, 18, 28\frac{1}{2}$
c   2, 6, 8, 14, 22

Investigating and generalising

2a   5, 9, 13
b   goes up in 4s
c   21, 33
6a   9, 11, 13
12a $4n + 1$
bi   41
bii   61

YEAR 8

Solving word problems

4   17 and 7

Identifying information

2b   Week 4

Breaking into steps

2c   381 hours
5   48

Establishing solutions

4   72
5c   48

Investigating and generalising

3a n^2
b   900

YEAR 9

Solving word problems

1   22 kg
11   23 and 11
25   50%

Identifying information

5   8

Breaking into steps

3a   Jack £7, Molly £5
b   Jack £3, Molly £9

Establishing solutions 1

1a   by adding the previous two numbers

Establishing solutions 2

1a $11\frac{1}{2}$
b $2A + B - C$, 4
c $A + B \times C$, 60

Investigating and generalising

4a   13.9 cm, 11.5 cm^2
b   23.9 cm, 34 cm^2
c   32.6 cm, 63.3 cm^2
11   56.25